A
TRUE-LIFE
ADVENTURE

SECRETS OF LIFE

WALT DISNEY

SECRETS OF LIFE

A TRUE-LIFE ADVENTURE

by **Rutherford Platt** and the Staff
of the Walt Disney Studio

Based on the Film Narration by
James Algar

ALSO IN THIS SERIES

THE LIVING DESERT
THE VANISHING PRAIRIE

FOREWORD

WHAT curious kinds of life may inhabit Mars and other planets? Do weird trees and flowers grow out there? Do people—or whatever you would call them—possess fantastic bodies and mysterious powers?

These are haunting thoughts, for man wants to know

the unknown. But until trips to Mars become feasible, we must be content to explore the mysterious worlds that exist right here on Earth.

In truth, landscapes of great wonder and beauty lie under our feet and all around us. They are discovered in tunnels in the ground, the hearts of flowers, the hollows of trees, fresh-water ponds, seaweed jungles between tides, and even drops of water. Life in these hidden worlds is more startling in reality than anything we can imagine on other planets. Some of Earth's own inhabitants are almost too startling for belief. They are graceful and gentle; they are horrible monsters; they are giants—or dwarfs. They communicate with each other by devices that are far beyond the reach of our senses.

Modern science helps us to explore these hiding places of nature and to study the activities of their inhabitants— playing and fighting, eating and mating, taking care of their babies—living life in full swing. And among those who make these explorations, none is a more understanding or more eloquent reporter than our present author.

As we read his accounts, we cannot but ask ourselves: How could this earth of ours, which is only a speck in the heavens, have so much variety of life, so many curious and exciting creatures?

Walt Disney

CONTENTS

At first, Earth glows red-hot.

Then rock cools and solidifies.

Photographs in this book were taken by the following:

STUART V. JEWELL
ROBERT H. CRANDALL
RUTHERFORD PLATT

FRAN WILLIAM HALL
HUGH A. WILMAR
TILDEN W. ROBERTS
ARTHUR S. CARTER
CLAUDE JENDRUSCH
ROY EDWARD DISNEY
MURL DEUSING
VINCENT J. SCHAEFER
WILLIAM M. HARLOW
WILLIAM A. ANDERSON
HUBERT A. LOWMAN
NORBERT WITKOWSKY
HAWAII NATURAL HISTORY
    ASSOCIATION

Illustrations on this page and the facing page by ART RILEY and JOSHUA MEADOR

Illustration on page 57 by DOROTHY HODGES. Reproduced from *The Pollen Loads of the Honey Bee*, published by The Bee Research Association, England

Water supplies oceans and ice.

Today's world has green forests and jungles.

The same kind of glacier that once covered the northern part of the United States can still be seen today in Greenland.

SECRETS HIDDEN
IN ROCKS

THE STORY of Earth is the story of change. Everything on the earth, whether it be animals or stones, glaciers or grass, mountains or oceans, is not quite the same from one day to the next. And given time—of which nature has plenty—everything on the Earth will eventually be transformed.

Fossils in the rocks tell the billion-year-old story of multitudinous forms of life that have flourished on the face of the earth for a time, then vanished. Grooves and scratches on the rocks tell where glaciers passed, a few thousand years ago. Before our eyes, not always visibly, mountains are rising and being worn down, valleys are being cut by rivers, forest lands are changing to desert, volcanoes are bursting into

life or going dormant, and the sea is restlessly breaking the edges of the land.

All this is happening now as it has happened in the past and will happen in millennia to come. Truly old Earth is a laboratory of marvels in which all things are at work, building and destroying, changing Earth as it has been changed through countless centuries.

A granite shoulder facing the sea, sculptured and polished by waves, is a monument of the war between sea and land. Its quartz crystals, six-angled like snowflakes, sparkle with colors. As waves beat on the granite year after year, grinding pebbles against it, the crystals crumble into sand. And the sand becomes sediment, settling to the sea bottom with dead animals and plants and other odds and ends of nature's refuse.

Sediment pressed down for thousands of years gradually turns to solid rock. The remains of living things caught in the sediment also may turn to rock, or leave their imprints, or even endure as bits of skeletons. So the great fossil detective story is written and hidden away—pictures and diagrams of animals and plants that lived in the unbelievably remote ages when the sediments were forming. Fossil-bearing rocks lie in layers, like pages of a book; usually the latest ones are on top, the older ones below.

It took daring and imagination to read this story in the rocks. For a long time people would not believe it. They tried to find other explanations for the shells, and for the bones of whales, embedded in rocks in the mountains of

Tons of ocean water grind and smooth the rocks along the shore.

Black areas on the map show where swamps formed ages ago in North America, during the Coal Age. Trees and ferns growing there died, were buried under layers of mud, and finally turned to coal.

Montana. And they disbelieved what they heard about the rounded boulders and glacier-ground bedrocks of New England. But the story was there, and would be told.

In America, two chapters—widely separated ones—of the book of the earth's crust give us a sense of the grandeur of the whole.

Millions of years ago a mountain range rose up from under the Atlantic Ocean. These mountains may have been as lofty as today's Alps. The center of these ranges was about 100 miles east of New York City. During the following 100 million years, which we call the Coal Age, the mountains crumbled and were washed down by torrential rains into the vast lowlands west of the mountains. Here flourished many early amphibian ancestors of the dinosaurs. The weather was warm and wet, forests of ferns and trees grew up, fell, and sank into the mud. More sediments, more plant and animal debris, buried the trees deeper as centuries passed. Cut off from air, squeezed under tremendous pressures, these plants instead of decaying became the carbon which is now our coal.

Compared to the Coal Age, the Ice Age was yesterday. Only 25,000 years ago glaciers were pushing southward over the northern United States. This was only one of several ice invasions known to have occurred during the

White area on the map shows the farthest extent of the Ice Age glacier which covered all of Canada and New England, as well as Greenland, parts of Alaska, and some of the Middle Western states.

Surf is constantly pounding and wearing away the shoreline.

Pleistocene period. One slow, irresistible finger of ice, 2,000 feet high, thrust down as far as New York harbor. As the slow glaciers bulldozed and ground their way through the mountains, the splitting ice boomed, great rocks crashed down the slopes, and landslides roared. Today, in our quieter world, we can thank the glaciers for grinding up rock and spreading sediments for the soil which was to be filled with millions of miles of roots belonging to the plants and trees the Earth supports today.

The constant changing of this world is hidden behind the calm of mountains, the colors of sunsets, the glory of clouds and the blue sky. But look more closely. On the sea, somewhere a gale is brewing; a glassy calm turns into a rhythm of sea waves, and then into the thunder of surf. Quiet ponds, blue eyes of the land, also have their secrets. Many are filling up with sediments, growing shallower, some day to disappear. Trees are on the move, throwing out seeds to walk across the land. Glaciers in the north country are shrinking, leaving gravel beds which will eventually turn into green meadows, where flowers bloom and bees buzz after nectar.

It is in the very midst of this story of life that we live. We are the actors in it, but also we are the audience, and we can enjoy the show.

Retreating glaciers melted, leaving lakes and pools behind.

Soil nourishes the green growing things that support all animal life, as well as man himself.

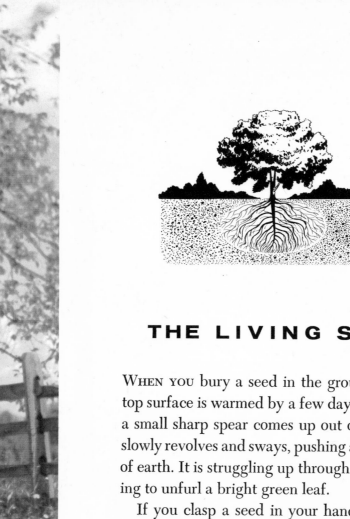

THE LIVING SOIL

WHEN YOU bury a seed in the ground, and the top surface is warmed by a few days of sunlight, a small sharp spear comes up out of the soil. It slowly revolves and sways, pushing aside crumbs of earth. It is struggling up through the soil, trying to unfurl a bright green leaf.

If you clasp a seed in your hand, it will not grow. But in the quiet, dark soil, it begins to move and to develop beautiful forms and colors. This tells us the soil possesses its own magic—a secret of life.

The seed that was put into the soil seemed to be hard and dry. It looked utterly lifeless. What happened to it during the long months it lay hidden under its covering of soil?

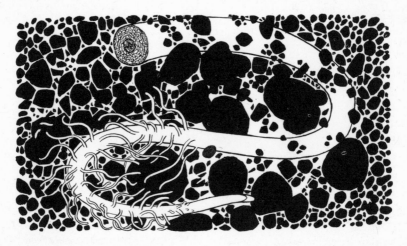

At the root tip, countless root hairs spring out to grasp tiny particles of wet soil, soaking up water and minerals.

Of all the strange events that take place in the zigzagging caverns of the soil, the most surprising are the travels of the roots and the threads that burst out from their tips. They are the fastest-growing and the longest part of the plant. A scientist measured the area of the roots and hairs of a single plant of winter rye, and found that they had a surface one hundred times greater than all the parts that grew above the ground.

Even more unbelievable was the speed with which they lengthened. They grew three miles of new roots per day. Those are the regular roots—the brown, stringy ones. Added to them are billions of microscopic white root hairs that slide through spaces between grains of soil. With these added, the rate of root travel of this single plant of

Leaves fall to earth and decay, enriching the soil.

Rainstorms bring water for the soil to store up underground.

winter rye averaged the astounding total of nearly 53 miles per day.

In all the wonders of life nothing is more marvelous than this power drive of roots through the soil. How can a thing as slender and soft as a thread penetrate the soil that seems so compact? What is the mechanism that makes their extended travels possible?

The root wears a hard little helmet at its point. This acts as a wedge. It is pushed forward with half a pound of pressure, and when inserted between grains of soil, expands with eight pounds of pressure. The tip controls the activity, thrusting and steering the course, guiding the root in its twistings and turnings. It goes toward wetter ground and avoids the drier. It detours around larger stones and the root follows behind like a snake, taking the easiest path.

We think of roots as we see them when a tree is blown over—heavy, brown, crooked wood from which brown strings dangle. This is the anchor part. It forces its way between cracks of rocks, if it must, without any sign of disturbing the soil.

But the roots which touch the life-giving magic of the soil are not tough, heavy, and brown. They are white hairs as fine as the silk of a spider web. Each has a point as sharp as a needle. The helmet at the tip of the growing root has butted and wedged its way forward and discovered fresh caves between the soil grains, with walls glistening with water. Then these hairs spring out from the root just behind the helmeted tip. Water acts on the root hairs like a magnet. Billions of thirsty threads poke into every space. When one touches a grain of sand coated with water, it spreads like a tiny baseball mitt to take hold of the grain and soak up the water.

What we call dirt seems solid under our feet. But that is a great misunderstanding. One of the wonders of soil is that it is not solid at all. Grains of sediment are irregular, jagged shapes of different sizes, and do not fit tightly together. Pieces touch at countless points, making the ground firm; but spaces are everywhere between them.

In some places more than half the soil consists of spaces filled with air and water. The secret power of soil is in the spaces between grains. Think of the spaces as a vast system of connecting caves. The tiny soil animals and bacteria in the caves between the grains do not miss the sun. They spend their lives in the darkness of the jungles of root hairs, and get the energy of the sun indirectly. It comes to them as food from larger animals that go up into the world of sunlight part of the time, and return to the soil to live and die. Sun energy is also packed into leaves, twigs, and fruits. These fall and decay, and their energy is absorbed into the soil.

Soil spaces are air-conditioned. They never get too hot or too cold. There is always plenty of water. This may be in pools in the spaces where it is trapped. But usually the spaces of living soil do not hold water for long, because after a rain the water trickles down through the spaces. Most water is held as a shiny coating on the surfaces of grains of soil. There is so much invisible water in the air underground that the Weather Bureau would say it is on the point of raining—at 100% humidity.

The things that live in the soil never go hungry. There is always plenty of food at hand. Soil is the world's mixing bowl; it brings together all the elements life needs, cooks them, and makes them ready for all the billions of plant roots that must feed on them.

This is the way power in the storage battery of the soil is made: the power is first delivered to the earth as sunlight. Scientists estimate the energy delivered to the whole earth at over 400 million-million horsepower a day. A large part of the sun's energy is caught by green leaves, where it is stored. When autumn comes the leaves turn brown and die. The wind sweeps them from the trees. They fall to earth and decay in the soil, where their locked-up energy is released and can be used in the earth's mixing bowl of life.

This chemical food energy is what is meant by the fertility of the soil.

As the root hairs take water and nourishing minerals from the earth, the leaves let water evaporate through their pores.

As the wind blows, grass seeds are scattered far and wide.

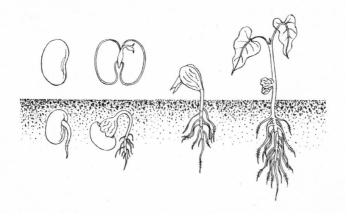

SECRETS OF SEEDS

IF WE look through our magic window into the depths of plants and explore the hiding places among the green leaves, we learn the secrets of seeds. Seeds are actually complete plants that can move around and travel as far as animals.

Every plant is engaged in the great project of making miniature copies of itself. Each copy consists of only one or two leaves, a stem, and a tiny root. The whole copy is microscopically small, but size does not matter because it has the mysterious power to grow as big as the plant that made it. This is true whether the plant is to be a giant sequoia or a violet.

The tiny plant is surrounded with a nugget of food, and wrapped in a tough weatherproof

Plants and trees package their seeds in many different kinds of envelopes, with devices that help them scatter themselves abroad.

cover. We call it a seed. Often the outside cover is equipped with wings or parachutes or fins that help it coast, whirl, glide, or ride the winds. In this way the miniature plant can go traveling.

The root of the plant inside the seed is not attached to the soil; its leaf is not exposed to the sunlight. But it is a complete living plant, though asleep like a hibernating animal. It can live indefinitely on the nugget of pure food packed around it. When it finds a place to grow, it bursts the tough outside wrapper, thrusts down its root, thrusts up its stem, unfurls its leaf, and develops its power to make another member of this green world.

All the colors of desert flowers, all the green sweep of the countryside, all the swaying treetops of the forest are

When the seed pod of the cottonwood tree bursts feathery seeds float off on the spring wind.

The red maple seed (left) glides on rigid wings. The seed of the ailanthus tree whirls on wings curved like a propeller.

devoted to this act of creation. To make seeds, thousands of miles of roots push through caverns of the living soil, thousands of gallons of water are gathered, filtered, and lifted up through stems and trunks; countless leaves make food of air and water with the power of sunlight; flowers sparkle in fields and woods; their stamens and pistils move and turn; while tons of pollen grains are transported from flower to flower.

Obviously, these seeds must possess a secret for going places and discovering suitable spots to grow in.

One reason for their success is that plants gush seeds in unlimited numbers. A single plant of red clover only a few inches tall turns out 500 copies of itself. The weedy crabgrass makes 90,000 seeds on each plant. Pigweed gives the crabgrass tough competition by moving into real estate with a million seeds per plant. One orchid was estimated to grow 3,770,000 seeds on a single plant. Orchids grow high up in trees, and their seed must find a limb which is wet, where the bark is slightly decayed. To win out where the odds are so great, the orchid makes millions of seed copies as light as the finest powder.

You might suppose a tree could not outwit a forest fire. But the knobcone pine can save its seed even while the parent tree is crashing in flames.

The witch hazel shoots out its seeds like cannonballs.

A raging forest fire destroys the adult trees.

Unlike most pine trees, which open the cone's shutters and let the seeds slide out when ripe, the knobcone holds its ripe seeds sealed inside the cones. The cone is almost as hard as rock. It protects its live seeds for as long as fifty years in a safe deposit vault. The cones hug the trunk of the tree so that as it expands with the passing years, it swallows its own cones by growing around them.

The little copies of the tree inside its seeds are forever waiting. If the tree dies, the seeds remain alive inside. Only a fire can release them.

When that disaster occurs and the knobcone forest is burned, the cones explode like popcorn. This explosion

Knobcone shoots out its seeds into the hot ashes.

flings out seeds to grow in the ashes, after they have been cooled and wet by rain.

A fire is a calamity for a forest, but this wonderful pine tree has built-in fire insurance. As the fire is dying, another forest is planted.

We are proud of our inventions. They solve many problems of living and save trouble. Plants also have problems and troubles, and they have also made marvelous mechanical inventions for meeting them.

In the early days of evolution when fewer plants were fighting for a place in the sun, it was easier for seeds to find places to grow. Simple seeds traveling by air and

Fluffy seeds of milkweed are blown on the wind (left) after the milkweed pod has launched its seed parachutes.

water kept plants spreading over the land. Trouble arose when, after millions of years, many new plants evolved. Many plants found themselves not on mountainsides and open prairies, but living in crowded jungles, or thickets, where there was too much shade. The places where seeds could take hold were few. Plants had to find ways for their seeds to travel farther, and they had to find a way to shoot them out beyond the shady areas.

This is a modern problem. It calls for modern mechanical inventions to give seeds the means to travel farther and faster and to have direction.

Parts of the plant which surround the seed when it is being made can be remodeled into any number of peculiar inventions. Every seed is formed inside a little pocket of the plant called an ovary. The base on which the ovary rests may swell up into an apple or pear. These additions to the seeds can be so delicious they will be eaten by birds and other animals that will carry them off, and distribute them. Acorns and other nuts just exactly fit the jaws of squirrels, who run off with them, bury them for future use, forget some of them—and the seed grows.

Other parts—such as petals and sepals, stamens and pistils—can be remodeled into gadgets to help the seed. The big hooks on burdock hitchhike on the fur of animals, or on passing trousers or skirts. Seeds of burr, marigold, tick-trefoil, or Spanish needles, can go for a walk in the same way. Instead of using hooks, some plants make their seeds sticky. Or seeds may be coated with an oil that certain ants love to eat. This causes the ants to cart them off to their underground tunnels, where some of the seeds will take root and grow.

Of all the inventions plants "think up" to help their copies go places, most unbelievable are the sling-shots, catapults, spring mechanisms, exploding parts, and cannon.

The wild oat seed has an overcoat outside its regular seed coat, with a long stiff bristle called an awn, bent in the middle with a knee that makes it look like the leg of a grasshopper. The awn is the leg of the seed. It has no muscles, but in cool moist weather the knee will bend. In the warm, dry sun of midday, the leg will straighten with such force that the seed is lifted over rough ground. In this way the seed can even burrow itself into the earth!

A honey bee rapidly drinks up all the nectar in this blossom's many florets, fills his pollen baskets, and flies away.

SECRETS
OF FLOWERS

WHEN YOU stop to think of it, each flower is an astonishing invention. Consider their shapes and sizes, their rich colors, the lines and spots painted on them. A fresh flower is never still. Sepals fold and unfold, petals swing open, stamens lift and curve, pistils thrust out, nectar overflows. The secret purpose is to make sure pollen of one plant is transported to the pistil of another plant of the same kind, at the moment its spark is alive.

To make seeds, a plant needs the cooperation of other plants just like itself. They must reach out and touch. They do this with a magical powder called pollen, the yellow dust which falls out of stamens when they burst. Cottonwood trees, oaks, and corn plants, too, load their pollen into tassels. You can see it when you shake the golden dust of these tassels into your hand.

You can see pollen when trees "smoke" in early spring. Clusters of tiny knobs appear at the ends of twigs, especially toward the top of the tree. When a breeze shakes them, jets of yellow dust puff out. This occurs on maples early in April, a few days later on elms and pines, while the oaks are last.

The way certain flowers pick a particular kind of insect to deliver their pollen is an astonishing secret of life. Without realizing it, the insect operates the seed-sparking machine like an expert. Sometimes it steps on a pedal with the right amount of pressure to make a derrick swing down and deposit pollen on the insect's back. Or it pushes walls outward to cause stamens or pistils to pop out and touch its stomach, back, or head. Many flowers use a piston-and-cylinder mechanism where pollen is kept in a tube and pushed out by the piston, so that fresh pollen is always kept ready for the next insect.

Bees, butterflies, moths, and wasps are not the only creatures that carry pollen to flowers. Some flowers use birds, bats, beetles, or flies to operate their beautiful machinery. Each of the biggest and most expensive orchids has an elaborate machine, designed for its particular insect only.

A grain of pollen is invisible to the naked eye. It is only a single cell. Yet into this tiny structure are distilled all the personality and characteristics of the parent plant.

While drinking nectar, a yellow sulphur butterfly brings pollen to a wildflower.

Tassels of the corn plant drop pollen on the silk below.

Up to the time of pollinating, the life stream of the plant flows unbroken from its own inner growth through trunk, stem, leaf, and flower. But with the maturing of the pollen, this life stream is broken. To bridge the gap in the life cycle, plants need help from outside forces. In the case of the smoking trees and grasses, that force is the wind.

When pollen lands in a flower of the same kind of plant from which the pollen came, it sets in motion machinery that matures the seed. If the pollen grain lands on another kind of plant, nothing happens. This bit of plant wisdom is merely one of nature's countless wonders.

This can be seen when corn pollen lands on pink silk at the top of the ear. When a pollen grain lands on a sticky thread of silk, it forms a tube that eats its way into the thread. If it lands near the outer end of the silk, this tube may lengthen by ten inches as it travels down the inside of the thread. It is striving to reach an egg cell at the base of the thread, and to turn this into a grain of corn.

The outside cover of a pollen grain is almost indestructible armor. It does not decay like other parts of plants. Pollen grains thrown out by plants that lived on earth 250 million years ago, during the Coal Age, have retained their different shapes, even though they are no longer alive.

Each thread of silk leads to a single kernel of corn.

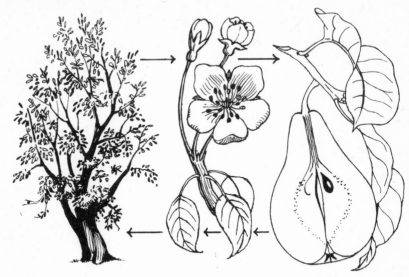

The pear tree flowers in spring. After insects have brought pollen to its blossoms, the petals drop off. The walls of the seed cases swell to form a pear. Inside the fruit is the seed; from it a new tree will grow.

Pollen must go to work soon after it leaves the plant, because it loses its power when wet. To keep pollen dry in the rain, Queen Anne's Lace tips its horizontal table of flowers to a vertical position.

Brightly colored flowers invite various creepers, walkers, and fliers to carry their pollen. Such plants make their pollen grains sticky so that it will cling to insect faces, bodies, and legs. These coincidences are very odd indeed. Neither insect nor plant thought them up or planned them. Flowers and insects just grew up together. They have succeeded because the presence of insects and plants together at the right time and place made life possible for both of these interdependent forms of life.

In a microscope, a grain of pollen looks like an exquisite jewel. All plants shape pollen differently. Pine pollen has a pair of air-filled bladders that helps it float through the air. Other grains resemble minute canoes, footballs, dumb-bells, or crystals. Pollen changes its shape and size. The tough exterior coat is flexible with slits and pleats. When wet, it swells up. When dry, it shrinks to its original shape.

Although plants are unable to move, they outwit the animal population. They use its millions of legs to run around, its millions of wings to fly, its millions of bodies to move pollen from one pinpoint to another. Plants manage to have their spark of life collected and delivered to the right spot at just the right time. In all the ages of flowering plants, the system of the flower has never failed to per-petuate its kind and to clothe the earth.

These are examples of grains of pollen, highly magnified. No two types of plants shape their pollen grains alike.

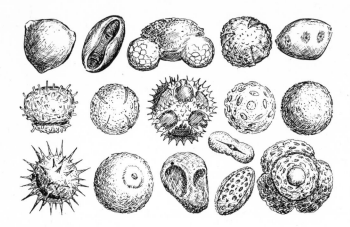

A flower garden is a paradise for bees.

SECRETS OF BEES

A HONEY BEE is the most remarkable creature on earth. Everybody likes to see a bee capering among the flowers. It stands out in a crowd of insects because it is bigger than most of them, makes a bigger buzz, and never stops working.

But people are afraid of being stabbed. A bee's stinger is a spear that shoots from its rear. It has nine barbs on each side, split down the middle. The two halves slide back and forth on each other. This double spear is enclosed in a sheath worked by a strong muscle. The two halves slide back and forth with a pumping action. When the spear enters the flesh, the barbs hold fast. A bee is light and can't take hold strongly with its tiny claws. It could not sink its spear through tough skin at one blow. Instead, the spear must pump itself in.

When the bee tries to pull away, it is fatally wounded, tearing itself away from its own stinger. Bees are not anxious to sting people. They sting only when scared or angry. When the ordinary honey bee stings it dies; the barbs cause the spear to remain in the body of its victim, and as the stinger is torn away, it pulls the bee's vital organs along with it.

Few people know the exciting mystery hidden in that black-and-yellow ball of buzz. It packs a lot of life power. A drop of honey is a high-octane fuel that drives the bee to flower after flower, while it sparks their seeds. Bees and flowers are two parts of the same life, like heads and tails of a coin. This amazing creature-and-plant team, coordinated to an almost unbelievable degree, is one of nature's most wonderful creations.

A bee is the only flying creature built to carry heavy freight. It has storage space and lifting power to transport syrup, pollen, and varnish. It easily manages the heaviest airborne cargoes. All other fliers (birds, bats, and other insects) carry only themselves through the air, except for light air mail such as twigs and worms which birds carry in their beaks occasionally.

Man's freight planes carry a pay load of about 25 per cent of their weight. A bee can carry almost 100 per cent. Man's planes have enormous wings for lifting and gliding, but they do not have power to move forward. They lift only when the plane is going fast enough to make suction on top. The bee has short wings on a fat body. It cannot

Honey bees sip nectar with a hollow tube called a proboscis.

glide, but it can move up, down, or stand still in mid-air. It does not have to move forward for its wings to lift it. It needs no propeller or jet, because the wings both lift and drive it forward in flight.

This is done by a marvelous mechanism. The short, wide wings beat at high speed with a weaving figure-8 motion. By changing the shape of the figure-8, the bee can drive itself forward, or stand still in the air in front of a flower and look it over.

The stubby wings can fold in a second when the bee dives into a flower or into one of the tightly fitting cells of the hive. It would be in a fix if it had long, rigid wings like a dragonfly's. A dragonfly never folds its wings, but it never dives into flowers; it just loafs on them. The bee has two pairs of wings, but even if you watch carefully, you would never see them. They are so close together their edges almost touch. For flying, a row of hooks on the forward edge of the rear wings fastens into a pleat on the edge of the front wings. This doubles the wingspread. They can be quickly unhooked and folded up like a lady's fan, or unhooked when the bee wants to whirl them as an electric fan, instead of using them for flying. Often a group of worker bees will use their wings as fans for ventilating the hive, or to warm it in winter, or to drive off the excess moisture in nectar, during the process of reducing this watery liquid to honey.

This flying machine has three places for storing cargo. One is the tank inside, which it fills by sucking up nectar syrup through a long tube from the inside of the flower's body. The other two are the baskets on its hind legs for carrying pollen. Who ever heard of a plane carrying freight on the landing gear? But the bee has been doing this since man first wrote about it in 3,000 B.C. It hasn't changed its equipment for carrying freight since.

The bee carries freight in one direction only. Outward bound, it needs only a speck of honey for fuel, enough to reach the goal, where it can find plentiful stores of honey and refuel. Honey is so powerful that a pinhead-sized speck of it will whirl the bee's wings for about a quarter of a mile.

Sometimes the nectar well is hidden deep in the flower's core.

If nectar is flowing strong and anthers are bursting with pollen, a bee can suck up a load of syrup in a minute. It can build two big, bulging loads of pollen in the baskets on its hind legs in three minutes. Often it may carry water in its honey tank, if the hive is thirsty. It may scrape resin off sticky buds and twigs, especially poplar, horse-chestnut, willow, and honeysuckle buds, and load this into the pollen baskets. This resin will be made into varnish to coat tree hollows, making all surfaces perfectly smooth, even at the points where the hive is attached. Resin is used also to stop up cracks and crevices.

When it has a load, the bee flies home at fourteen miles per hour with a tankful of nectar inside, and two bulging

Some flowers exactly fit the shape of the bee (left); others spread huge banquets of nectar and pollen for all comers.

bags of pollen swung below that keep it flying upright. A loaded bee cannot fly upside down. It is no acrobat like a housefly, which can run about on the ceiling and can even manage to fly upside down with ease.

The tank can be filled by sucking nectar through a tube. But how can the bee attach the loads of pollen to the outside of its hind legs without the help of a well-trained ground crew? It isn't just a matter of scooping up pollen grains and tossing them into baskets the way you gather apples. To keep loads from blowing away or falling out in mid-air, pollen must be moistened, pressed like a snowball, molded, tamped down, and evenly balanced on each leg. Moreover, it must be collected from many flowers. The way a bee can collect and load its pollen baskets in three minutes is an everyday accomplishment in his world, but it is a true marvel of animal skill.

To collect pollen, a bee dives into a flower, scrambles around, rolls over like a child playing in the surf. The splashing throws pollen grains all over its body, where they stick to feathered hairs. When the bee dives for nectar, it doesn't have to cut capers. Its body picks up pollen just by brushing past the pollen boxes that are usually held out in front of the flower on long trembling stems.

The bee leaves the flower, and, while hovering in mid-air, or swinging below the flower and hanging by one claw, it combs its face, the top of its head, and the back of its neck with its front legs. Even the bee's eyes collect pollen, as hairs grow out of its eyeballs. The bee has a

Bees are covered with hairs for gathering pollen.

special soft brush to remove this pollen. A reverse gulp brings up a speck of honey from the honey tank to moisten the pollen. The middle legs scrape off the middle of the body, reaching up over the back. Rapid combings and passings to the rear get the pollen onto the hind legs. The scrapings are caught in a comb with nine rows of bristles. The bee doubles up its legs. A huge rake passes through the rows of bristles, pulling the pollen into a press made by the knee joint. When the bee bends its knee, the jaws of the press open; when it straightens its leg, the jaws close, and the pollen is pressed and pushed up into the pollen basket. The pollen basket is a shallow trough in the middle of the hind leg, located just where it widens like the blade of a paddle. To hold the load securely in place, there are many curving hairs around the edges. They serve to hold the bee's bulging load of pollen securely in place, just as stakes are used to contain a full wagonload of hay.

There is a single rigid hair in the center of the basket that makes it possible to build twice as big a load. As the pollen ball grows bigger and bigger, the curving hairs surrounding it are pushed apart, and the load mounts above them. The long rigid hair in the center gives the load a core. It holds the big swelling ball of pollen together like a pole planted in the middle of a haystack.

After its body is covered with pollen, the bee scrapes and presses it into the two pollen baskets on its rear legs.

All this skill and equipment is useless unless the bee can get to the right place at the right time. Bees do not spend the night among the flowers. They wait in the hive until sunrise. They do not know which flowers will open pollen boxes and gush nectar the following morning, or where they will be located. Flowers bloom in different places every day. Every morning ten thousand flying freight cars get ready to go out and load up.

They will not start until they know the kind of flowers, and the direction and distance to those flowers. Somebody must give them flight instructions. This will not be the queen, as she never issues an order. Entirely occupied with laying eggs, she would not know about flowers, pollen, or nectar. She might spend a year in the hive and go out into daylight only twice in her life. The job of gathering nectar and pollen belongs to the worker bees.

Now perhaps a dozen bees go out in different directions and scout the countryside. They fly around in the vicinity of the hive in ever-widening circles. If there is an apple orchard, a field of poppies or alfalfa, or a garden of beans or peas close by, or a meadow blooming with clover, great is the excitement in the hive, and the whole army will be on the wing and ready to travel in a few minutes.

But the day's plunder may be some distance away. The scouts may have to search across miles of countryside. When one of these returns, it will tell the others exactly what kind of flowers are open, and give them a compass bearing for the direction and announce the distance to the

Bees fan their wings rapidly in the hive, driving off moisture from the nectar to reduce the watery liquid to honey.

spot. Many other creatures can communicate, but few can equal in clarity and usefulness the language that the honey bee has invented.

This sounds like a fairy tale, but life is that way, especially with bees. The fact that bees can talk to each other and give complicated instructions to a group of workers in the hive is a recent and startling discovery.

When a scout strikes it rich, it fills its tank, packs its baskets, and flies back to the hive. Others crowd around, pushing back like police lines to clear space for the scout.

If it begins with a weaving dance, turning left and right, it is saying, "Plenty all around! Go and get it!" In that case, the bees crowd up excitedly, touch the dancer with their antennae to pick up the odor of the flowers they must look for, and fly off.

But if the treasure is a long way off—perhaps a single tree or a small patch of flowers—that would be like finding a pinprick on the map, and the searchers could easily get lost. So the scout, instead of weaving, runs along a straight line, wagging its abdomen. At the end of the line—only an inch or so long, as not much space is cleared in the crowd—it turns left and circles back to the starting point. It runs straight forward again along the same line, circles right—and then repeats its message!

The straight line points directly at the flowers. The speed with which the speaker circles tells the distance. The farther off the flowers are, the slower it circles back. If it makes ten circles in fifteen seconds, the flowers are about 300 feet away. If it moves in slow motion—two circles in fifteen seconds—the flowers are around four miles away! The amount of honey or pollen is told by the wagging of the abdomen. If it shakes vigorously, the supply is abundant. If it shakes lazily, there is only a little, and just a few bees should go. The others, in that case, will wait for another scout's arrival.

This marvelous briefing of a big audience of bees was discovered by a patient scientist named Karl von Frisch. He spent years figuring it out.

Six-sided cells are storehouses for honey and pollen.

This little ball of life with its great flying power, its weird equipment for plundering flowers, its big eyes (two globes with 6,300 eyes in each bulge occupy most of its face) and its ability to communicate, does not have a life of its own.

We have been watching it by itself in order to get a close-up view of its secrets. But it does not exist that way. Unlike other creatures, it does not have babies and raise its own family, build its own home, eat its own food, or fight for its own life. The honey bee is a thing of sunshine and fresh air, and its buzz is the song of a summer day. It fits so beautifully into our world, and does such a fine job sparking the seeds of flowers, that it is hard to believe what a different world bees live in—the strange world of the hive.

The whole hive is like one animal, living in a beautiful home, with rows of six-sided rooms built of wax that looks like marble. In this building clusters a throng of bees. A small hive has twenty thousand, a middle-sized hive seventy-five thousand, and a big hive, two hundred thousand members.

This is not a city of many families; it is a single life. One extra-large bee that lives in the heart of it has produced all the bees of the hive. This is the queen who slaves to lay up one or two thousand eggs per day. Before we speak of her, let us see how the bees build the white bee building.

The trick is performed by younger bees under seventeen days old, which have not yet reached the stage of flying off to gather honey and pollen. If the comb is new, and there is no old comb to enlarge, they hang themselves in festoons from the roof of the hive or the hollow in the tree. One hooks its claws to the roof and another hooks on to the hind legs that dangle down. They look like watch chains looped from the ceiling. More and more bees hook their front legs to the hind legs of those above. The chains grow longer. As they sway and touch, the bees hook on right and left, forming a living curtain. Nobody knows why they hang up in this way, but the wax seems to come faster when the body is stretched out.

On each side of the abdomen are four wax pockets. After twenty-four hours of hanging, tiny slips of wax begin

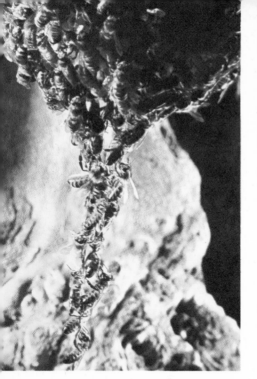

While making wax (left), bees hang in long, swaying chains. Nurse bees (right) feed baby worker bees in their cells.

to appear, like letters stuck in their pockets. When a bee feels its wax ready to come all the way out, it takes the letters out of its pockets, chews them, and pats on the wax where the comb is to be built. Sometimes the wax scales come fast, especially if many bees have hung themselves up at the same time. Wax scales litter the floor. The bees swinging on high regard this supply of wax as workmen would regard a load of lumber dumped near their job. The bees do not delay this building until the time the wax-making is fully completed. Instead, the lowest let go the legs of those above, drop to the floor, pick up the wax slabs and buzz up where the walls of the hive are rising.

A worker bee uses its head to ram pollen into a storage cell.

Honey bees enjoy the reputation of being architects and engineers because they build many rows of little rooms the same size, each one with three pairs of walls facing each other, so that they are six-sided. Such a building has a pattern like lattice or wallpaper, and it forms mysteriously under the feet of six-legged insects who run around and work constantly. They have no drawing boards, compasses, or rulers, but the job is well-measured and very strongly made.

Wax is reinforced by drawing long thin threads of varnish through it. The wax hardens around the threads, like concrete reinforced with wire. Varnish is also used on rough places in the hollow tree the bees brush against, going and coming. Cell walls are only 1/350th of an inch thick. It would be impossible to see a thread so fine. This makes a sharp edge—even for the feet of the bees—and since bees constantly run around on their comb, the top edges must be thickened. Extra wax is dabbed on, giving the walls a rounded coping. The outside of the building becomes a comfortable screen for them to run around on.

The secret of the bees' skill lies in the way they use natural forces. Soft materials like putty, clay, or warm wax will become very thin when you push against them from opposite sides. If a lot of holes in the soft stuff are pushed against each other at the same time, they form six-sided walls, particularly if the walls are extremely thin.

Bees start by just piling on wax, laid on like mud when a swallow builds a nest. The holes begin as rough cups, pressed in by the bee's body, and the cells will always be that size and exactly fit the shape of the bee. The work of shaping and finishing the cells is done by lots of bees in lots of holes, all pushing simultaneously against each other. They use heads, feet, bodies—smoothing, scraping, and ramming home the wax, which is kept warm by their bodies.

When nature pushes fluid materials together, they form six sides. That shape makes them cling the closest together without spaces between. Crystals are made this way. Snowflakes are all six-sided or six-pointed. You can see flat,

Since the drone bee will not feed himself, he is fed honey by a worker bee. Drone's eyes are more than twice as big as the worker's.

six-sided surfaces between soap bubbles where the round bubbles touch when sticking together. It is a strange and wonderful law of nature. It is this that makes the fine architecture of bee combs, when bees build the soft wax together, all working at the same time. It is simply the result of the bees getting into the little round cups they have made and pushing them together.

Bees never rest inside their cells. They lead most of their lives crowding the face of the comb and flying out to fetch nectar and pollen. Cells are used to raise babies and to store honey and pollen. Storage tanks are capped over with a neat little lid of wax when full. No attention is paid to them except in winter when food is scarce. Then the cap is torn off and honey or pollen, according to which the tank holds, is used by all the bees. The bee which takes honey out of a cell passes it around.

To prove that a bee never digests its food all alone, but rather that the whole hive digests food together, scientists fed six bees in a hive of 24,500 radioactive honey. After two days, all the bees in the hive were radioactive, from passing the treated honey from mouth to mouth.

Bees are ever busy collecting from flowers, building their wax home, storing up honey and pollen, and passing around food. But a few extra big bees never do any of these things. While the others are so busy that they never stop working, the drones, or male bees, are idle. They don't even take the trouble to reach into a tank of honey or pollen for food. They ask other bees passing food around to give them some. The drones are waiting to fly off into the sky just once, chasing after the queen. That is all the drone bee ever does in its entire life. It has no pollen baskets, but it does have bigger wings for flying power and bigger eyes to see the queen when she is a tiny speck flying through the air.

There is only one queen in the hive. Like the drones, she never collects from flowers, builds with wax, or passes food around. She is not lazy. She is as important to the hive as a heart is to an animal. The other members of the hive must depend on that one queen bee if the life of the group is to continue.

The queen is a special invention. Other bees work so hard that they don't have time to have children, so nature invented the queen who is different from all the others and who can have all the children.

While laying eggs, the queen bee is surrounded by attendants.

To keep a hive of many thousands of bees strong and healthy, several thousand babies must be born every day. For although the queen may live for five years, worker bees live only forty-one days, and it is the endless job of the queen to replace them as they die off. She spends most of her time walking across the face of the comb, and as she passes one six-sided cell after another, she pauses for a few seconds and drops in an egg. Her job takes so much energy that she must have attendants to feed her constantly.

When the queen is laying eggs, she is surrounded by a retinue of twenty-two bees making royal jelly. They face her, surrounding her like spokes of a wheel Their entire

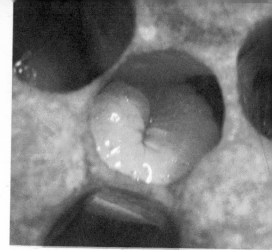

Blind grubs, fed by nurse bees, may eat 1300 meals a day.

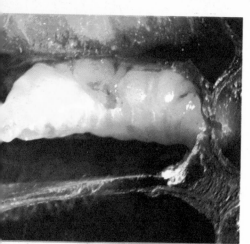

Then the grub spins a cocoon (left), becomes a milk-white nymph—

—sleeping in a wax cradle—and emerges as an adult worker.

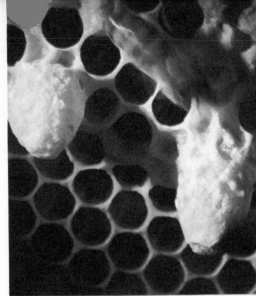

Workers pack royal jelly around grubs in large queen cells.

job is to keep feeding her royal jelly. As they pass the twelve-day old mark, they are replaced with younger bees, probably six-day-olds. For this remarkable food can be made only in the heads of adolescent bees.

The queen is not allowed to do any other work. In a day she can lay two thousand eggs, four times the weight of her own body. How can this be? She doesn't disappear and she is just as heavy, and ready to lay two thousand eggs more on the following day.

This is a strange secret of bee life. We find the answer in the mysterious power of royal jelly. This food looks like sticky cream, and the only place it can be made is in the head of a young bee. A bee must be the proper age to make royal jelly—from six to twelve days old. During that week, it chews pollen from the tanks in the comb, and mixes it

Workers attend the peanut-shaped cell until adult queen emerges.

with a peculiar kind of saliva to produce royal jelly. Wherever the queen turns while egg laying, the surrounding royal jelly feeders turn. Every twenty minutes she stops, and one of the retinue pumps her full of royal jelly, which makes her lay many eggs. The meal lasts three minutes. As the chief ingredient of royal jelly is pollen, we see how the dust that sparks plants turns into baby bees! And just as many plants would never mature their seeds without the bees to bring them the needed pollen, so some of this very pollen helps the queen bee lay her eggs.

If a queen dies or isn't laying enough eggs, the bees make a new queen. First they build an extra big cell. This queen cell is roughly dabbed together in a hurry. This special cell is peanut-shaped, and it is hung to the outside of the comb. The bees take an egg from a regular cell and put it in the queen cell. Sometimes they take a new-born baby bee. If it isn't over three days old, it is not too late to turn it into a queen instead of letting it hatch as a regular worker bee. This baby is fed all the royal jelly it can eat. It takes fifteen days to produce a queen, if the workers start with a fresh-laid egg. If they start with a one-day-old baby already hatched, they can have a full-grown queen bee in no more than eleven days.

The queen has a fine pair of wings, but she uses them only about twice in her long life: once to fly off on a mating flight, and again to fly away from her hive forever with a swarm, to start a new home. The grown-up queen stands around getting her bearings, and stretching her wings for three days. The bees keep feeding her royal jelly, but she can lay no eggs until after she has flown up into the sky with the drones and returned from her mating flight.

Meanwhile the drones have bestirred themselves for the first time in their lives. They prance around, clean their antennae again and again, clean their big eyes (the drones have 13,090 little eyes in each globe, more than twice as many as the ordinary bee has). If the weather is fair, around four o'clock in the afternoon of the fourth day after she became mature, the queen dashes off into the sky, with the drones after her. She returns to the hive a half hour later, ready to lay eggs for the entire colony of bees for the rest of her life.

When the drones return to the hive, demanding honey, the workers refuse to feed them and they starve.

Piping shrilly, the two queens begin their deadly battle.

If there is one time when a queen gets angry, it is when there is another queen around. This happens when a fresh queen has been produced while the old queen has not yet left the hive with a swarm. Then the two queens fight it out to the death.

The stinger of a queen is long and curved, and has no barbs. The queen can pull it out without killing herself, and sting her enemy again and again. A duel of queens is a terrible battle, with each trying to drive home the poisoned spear first. The bees understand that nature has decreed that a hive can have but one egg-layer. If a queen turns away, the others push her back to the attack. Fighting queens are not allowed to stop until one is killed.

When there are two queens in the hive, they often sound a high, clear note as a battle cry. The note of a queen who is fighting mad is called the piping of the queen. It is probably made because she is breathing hard in her excitement. The piping is made by forcing air through ten little holes in her sides. It is like the high note of a flute.

Often the older queen does not fight it out with the young queen, but when she finds out a new queen is being made in her hive, she prepares to leave and take along

Queen bees fight it out to the death.

Worker bees swarm as the queen leaves the hive.

whatever portion of the population will follow her and establish a new hive.

There is great excitement when a swarm is being stirred up. The hive neglects to go out and gather honey. Its whole routine is upset. The swarm may be a terrifying ball of thirty-five thousand bees. It shoots out of the hive, swirls around crazily and heads off. After roaring along, it comes to rest on a limb of a tree. It waits there for scouts to bring news of a protected place to build a comb. Then it flies there, starts taking wax letters out of its vest pockets, and bee life buzzes along again in its remarkable way.

Ants attack creatures many times their size. Here a black ant (left) attacks the huge velvet ant.

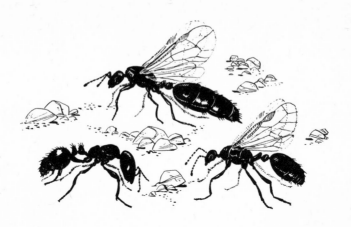

SECRETS OF ANTS

TAKE A GOOD look at an ant. It is made like three tiny bugs fastened together in a row on a piece of pipe. The one in front is the head; the middle one is the chest, or thorax; the one on the rear end, the abdomen, is the biggest of all.

If the ant is broken apart, each segment can go on living for a little while. Each has its own blood supply, its own breathing tubes, its own openings into the outer air closed by its own valves, and separate nerves to operate the muscles of each part. After the head is cut off, its jaws go on biting and its feelers go on feeling. The middle part, with six legs, can go on running and kicking. The rear part can continue to do what it was doing, whether laying eggs, stabbing with a stinger, or performing as a bottle of honey. Ants get into terrible fights. Because they have this type of body, if an ant is beheaded or its rear is torn off, the other two parts keep on fighting ferociously.

Ants have the biggest population of any dry land creature in the world, as they can fit themselves into any situation. They don't have to live in a certain kind of place, like a bee. Any soil anywhere in the world makes a home. A bit of rotten wood in a fallen log will do; or cracks in your house or barn. Ants are not particular. Bees eat only pollen and nectar, so that if there are no flowers around, there are no bees. But ants will eat many different foods found in large quantities everywhere.

Their chief food is dead insects, and of these there is an endless supply. One man watched a large family of ants, patiently counting the dead insects he saw lugged and pushed into the nest all morning. This averaged 28 per minute, or 13,500 bodies of all sizes in one eight-hour working day for the dinner table of that one family.

If dead insects are out of season, ants will readily turn to other varieties of food.

An apple or any fruit bruised by falling to the ground makes a luscious dish. Ants like food to be soft and squashy. They will not chew through the stretched, polished skin of an apple. They love seeds of grasses and berries. They wait for decay to cook them because seeds have tough coats. Some ants plant seeds, and when they start to sprout, bite off the root tip to keep them from growing,

The red ant is the black ant's deadliest enemy.

Before this newly fledged termite's wings have dried out enough for him to fly away, he falls prey to a hungry ant.

and they have a garden full of delicious fresh vegetables, available in endless supply.

Ants pass up fresh pollen which is a kind of crystal and hard. They cannot make pollen mush like bees, but they like honey. They lick sweet juices off leaves, and sap coming from a wound in a stem, and sweet syrup off other insects. They take nectar from flowers if they can, but flowers seem to know this, for many put up obstacles to ants crawling in. These flowers reserve their nectar for bees. They erect bristles that stop crawling ants like a barbed-wire entanglement. Some flowers defend nectar with gummy places, for no little insect can walk if its feet are stuck. Others dangle flowers from shaking, slippery stems, which knock off an ant before it can get to the flower. Ants are not bothered when they cannot obtain nectar from flowers, because they have so many varieties of food to choose from.

Suppose we watch an ant take a dead moth home. The fat body is twenty-seven times as big as the ant, and to make matters worse, stiff wings stick far out on each side. The route lies through a thicket of grass. The ant cannot follow a path down on the ground, because the grass stems would block the outstretched wings. It has to be up high with more open space, where the moth can be tipped up or down, turned this way and that. The job it is doing can be compared to a man's carrying an airplane through the thick treetops of a dense, matted jungle.

It is difficult to know how long the process will take. As the ant gets closer to home, perhaps others will smell the food and come out to help their companion with the terrible job of pulling the huge moth through the towering jungle and out onto a clear pathway leading to the anthill.

It is thickness of muscle, not length, that gives strength. The strong man has bulging muscles. An ant's muscles are thick and short. But more than strength is needed to get the moth home. The ant does not try to carry it. It drags, pushes, pulls, up-ends the load. It runs from side to side, in front or behind, working like a demon, never pausing. It

The ant's catch is stolen by a ground beetle.

has six legs to brace against the grass while it nudges the thing with its head. It can take a stand with three legs and use the others to support the load or as levers. It keeps up a rapid fire, tapping the moth's body and the grass with its feelers, sizing up the situation every instant. The moth mysteriously keeps moving—bumping and lurching toward the very place where the ant wants it to be.

With its long legs spread apart, and its body hung low, an ant is built for super-leverage, strong bracing, powerful dragging, pushing, and pulling. It even uses its elbowed feelers for support.

Its six legs—two pullers, two supporters, two pushers—

make it easy to understand why ants are so strong for moving heavy loads. They may work singly or tackle a major problem together. They can quickly bring pebbles from underground—pebbles which a man, if he were the size of an ant, would use a bulldozer to move. Ants can maneuver the rocks to clear their tunnels, and also make circular walls around the home entrance for protection. For ants are the world's greatest tunnelers and diggers, and their underground galleries and rooms are built to last for years, with special chambers built on various levels, to be used as apartments and storehouses for ant eggs or surplus supplies of food.

A boulder-sized pebble, weighing many times more than both these red worker ants, is easily removed from their tunnel.

A worm snake glides into the anthill, eating a baby ant.

Ants protect themselves from enemies better than any animal on earth. Even a keen-eyed bird has trouble picking up a target that disappears while you look at it. An ant is not helpless even when a beetle, an earthworm, or a snake burrows into the nest. One small snake, called a worm snake, will glide through ant tunnels looking for rooms where the ant's babies are hidden. Then the ants carry their babies through the connecting galleries into rooms deeper underground. Others attack the monster without hesitation. Although they are pigmies in comparison to the enemy, they put up a terrific fight: kicking, biting, stabbing, slashing, and cutting. For ants will attack anything that attacks them, regardless of size.

Often ants meet grasshoppers in the grass. The grasshopper has its eardrums down its forelegs, so that it can hear every little sound in the grass. When the big fellow looms up and stares down at them, the ants are maddened. One may point its rear end at the grasshopper and use its stinger like a firehose. It squirts a silent, invisible spray of stinging poison as far as eighteen inches. Then it is time for the grasshopper to become maddened, and to pull the springs of his mighty hind legs, and leap out of sight. Ants, with their tearing jaws and hidden stingers, have many ways of making giants mind their own business, and never hesitate to use any of their fighting equipment.

The ants attack their huge enemy fearlessly.

The endless series of galleries and rooms in which ants live may house several hundred thousand creatures. Called a colony, it is more like a family, because the throng often consists of children of one queen. Ant queens do not murder another queen if she turns up, as do queen bees, so ant nests may have several families living together. But they must all smell the same way, because this smell is paid out along their hunting trails. No matter how many trails crisscross, each ant can find its way back to the underground home from which it set out.

Ants that are busy digging tunnels, hauling food, and running trails never have wings. But in August, certain ants sprout wings! These are males and queens, going off to lay eggs. On a clear, calm afternoon these winged ants fly off on a mating trip into the sky. After this flight, the males drop to the ground; they can't hide, with their wings. They must hobble around until another insect or a bird finds them and eats them.

The queen also drops to the ground, but nature has attached her wings so that they can be easily torn off. She grabs them with her jaws and front feet and soon she is helpless and alone, far from the anthill where she has been carefully tended by nurses and workers.

Because she came through the air, there is no odor trail to find the way home. She must dig a hole as fast as she can. She is not a tunnel digger, so it is hard work. Her jaws are worn down, her hairs scraped off, her smooth armor scratched and bruised. She must dig before a bird spots

Worker ants take excellent care of the baby ants. Nurse ant (right) allows a tiny mite to ride atop her head.

her. When the hole is deep enough, she pulls a stone or some dirt over her and snuggles down and lies there for eighty-seven days in the quiet darkness until all her eggs have hatched. After that she has many children to do the digging, and real tunneling can start.

Ant tunnels are clean, round tubes. They are used as subways for the ants to get to rooms where they lay eggs or store food. The idea is to make it easy for the worker ants to carry their eggs and babies from one room to another if an enemy turns up.

Ants live a long time compared to other insects. A bee dies in six weeks, but ants live for years. The colony can grow hundreds of thousands of ants with a vast system of

This is an ant in the third, or pupal, stage of growth. It takes 87 days for ants to develop from egg to larva to pupa, and reach maturity.

tunnels, if not disturbed. Four months after the first eggs hatched, a new crowd of stronger tunnelers appear. Their swiftly passing polished bodies smooth the tunnels. These ants arch roofs of rooms and flatten floors. Two years later the large operation needs special guards. These turn up from the eggs that never stop hatching, and soldier ants stand at the entrances. Three years after the lost queen first dropped to the ground, some ants sprout wings, another flight goes off into the sky, another queen drops to earth, and starts furiously digging away for a new nest. Soon she will have established another flourishing colony of ants just like the one she left behind—the formula nature uses to scatter ant nests all over the world.

The giants that invade the ants' tunnel systems are not their most dangerous foes. All the cruel weapons, their fierce strength, and their stabbing and poisoning equipment are chiefly used against well-organized armies of other ants.

Great battles take place between ants again and again in summer. Let us watch a family of familiar black ants going about their business, running their maze of tunnels, raising hundreds of children, lugging in dead insects, and preparing for that great event when the winged ones will fly off on their once-in-a-lifetime flight into the blue sky, so another ant queen can begin a new ant colony.

One day an ugly stranger turns up at the tunnel of these black ants. He knows there are hidden rooms filled with

When danger threatens, nurse ants pick up larvae in their jaws and move them to safety in another part of the anthill.

The ferocious battle of the red and black ants begins.

white bundles of black ant babies. The stranger is richly
colored, brown-red tinged with purple. His jaws protrude
far out on each side of his head like enormous curving
scimitars, made to slash and pierce the armor of ants. This
is the face of the horrible Amazon ant, and the black ants
know it spells trouble for the whole colony. For he will
soon return, bringing an army of enemies with him.

When they know the red ants are nearby, the blacks
begin to stop their holes with stones and dirt. They scatter
pebbles and debris so that they will not give away the
location of their entrances.

Perhaps 200 feet away over the hill, the red ants are seething with excitement. Their scouts, searching the countryside, singly or in squads of four or five, leave an odor trail back from the front door of the blacks' hideout to the door of the home nest. This is the trail the red marauders will follow as they begin their march.

Now the reds pour out of their tunnels and line up in compact regiments. The column moves straight toward the home of the blacks. Arriving on the scene, the reds break ranks, ferociously pulling out plugs and tearing covers off tunnel entrances. They probably find the holes with their sense of smell. When the tunnels are opened, there is panic underground. The reds invade the galleries and snatch up babies. The blacks also snatch up their

Red ants swoop down on their enemies, slashing and stinging.

babies and carry them from room to room, trying to find a safe place for them.

Soon both reds and blacks pour out of the tunnels. Many have jaws full of white bundles. These are babies (pupae sound asleep) easily mistaken for eggs. The blacks are wildly looking for a place to put their bundles, while the reds form a single column and head straight for home, still holding the white bundles tight in their jaws.

The blacks do not let the reds keep their single-column march. They attack, and a terrible battle is joined. Reds and blacks slash with scimitars, stab with stingers, squirt poison vapors, bite off heads and legs. The two parts left after the head is cut off go on fighting. The field of battle is littered with pieces of ants and white bundles fallen to the

Ants continue fighting, even when bitten in two.

The blacks fight savagely to drive off the red invaders.

ground. The chances are the blacks outnumber the reds and will drive them off, pick up the babies, and put them back in the nest. Then they remove the dead bodies, and put the anthill back in order again.

Another kind of red ant, the red formica, makes war in a mob, instead of forming columns. They form a waving front several feet or yards across and ripple along, searching for black ant nests. They have been seen to go out raiding forty-four times during July and August. On six raids they found no nests, but from twenty-five expeditions they brought back great numbers of white bundles of babies. The reds bring them up as red ants, and the captured babies will work the same way and just as hard as they would for their own family. Ants are quick to forget, and soon after a battle, life goes on as usual.

Parasol Ants

People are proud of their vegetable gardens. They like to grow fine heads of cabbage, juicy red tomatoes, sweet, tender corn. But when it comes to the most delicious and nourishing vegetable cultivated in any garden, the prize goes to the ants. Not all ants, just a few that have learned to produce such a fine vegetable so rich in protein and sugar that they can give up eating insects and live on the garden crop. No other animal lives on food exactly like the food of these leaf-cutter, or parasol, ants. Let us see what sort of prize vegetable they raise.

Since ants are underground dwellers, they pick a special kind of plant. Green-leaved plants cannot grow in darkness, but mushrooms thrive where it is dark, damp, and cool. The underground part looks like cotton, and the ants prune it so it never grows the mushroom umbrella we see above ground.

This mushroom cotton makes luxurious gardens. The gardens look like bath sponges, full of holes where ants run in and out, and where fresh air can circulate. Mushroom cotton, treated with chemicals from the mouths of ants, causes clear, shiny heads of a mysterious vegetable to bubble out. The ants snip off these bubbles and eat them. They lay eggs on the cottony threads and when they hatch, it is as though they were lying in a bed of cabbages. The babies devour the crop all about them. Since this mushroom cotton grows only on fresh leaves fertilized

Parasol ants, or leaf-cutters, carry leaves to their underground gardens.

Mushroom cotton grows on leaves hanging from the ceiling.

in a particular way by ants, they keep cutting round pieces of leaves and carrying them back to their galleries. The parade of ants holding round green bits of leaves high overhead is the curious sight that gives them the name of parasol ants. The ant mushroom garden must be kept clean and pure. Dust must not spoil the delicate flavor of its vegetables, and germs would bring all sorts of weeds, spores, and bacteria into their neat vegetable garden. So while bigger ants are out cutting and carrying leaves, little ants are continually cleaning both the trees outside, as well as the underground tunnels, where the leaves are hung, covered with their growth of mushroom cotton.

Honey Cask Ants

Indians digging in the dry Southwest struck what looked like little green grapes. As they dug deeper, they kept finding more grapes down to about six feet. The grapes were juicy and sweet. But how in the world could they grow buried in the ground? The answer tells one of the strangest secrets of life in the darkness of ant caverns.

The juicy things were not grapes. They were storage bottles for honey. These bottles had feet that could wiggle, and bodies and heads attached, with waving feelers.

The stomach of the honey-cask ant is swollen with honey.

Primitive man made wine bottles and water jars out of leather. But the bottles the Indians found were live animals. They were ants which had agreed to drink all the honey brought to them, until they were swollen as round as a ball, and to give a drink of this to any ant that asked them for a meal.

These honey ants live on honey alone, but honey dew is plentiful for a few weeks only. Ants get it by stroking the backs of aphids—plant-sucking insects that make syrupy honey dew—or from gall lumps. Gall lumps are nests of insects which suck sap from oak trees, and turn it to honey dew. The syrup these insects make oozes out of the gall in droplets, during the night.

The ant family which depended on honey dew as its only food would die of starvation when honey was out of season unless some way were found to store it up. Ants can not build wax reservoirs, like bees, so some of them became honey bottles.

A honey bottle ant is called a replete, meaning "filled up." In a big family of honey ants, 300 repletes may be filled with honey syrup. They are ordinary workers, and are not born with special equipment for this job. We do not know whether a boss selects them or whether they step up and offer their services. From the time they start becoming repletes, they never go outside their caverns. Other ants do all the rushing around involved in locating and collecting the stores of delicious honey dew, for the repletes are little more than living storage bottles.

An ant starts turning into a honey bottle when young, before the armor of its body hardens. Then its skin can stretch. The honey stomach is in the rear, or abdomen. Its head and chest remain the same, but as more ants bring it a drink, its rear swells and swells until it is as round as a grape. It hangs itself up to the roof of the cavern, holding on with the claws of its front feet. Dangling there, it can only wave its legs. It is too fat to move. If the honey bottle gets accidentally knocked off, other ants use strength and skill to carry it up and hook it to the ceiling again. The others take good care of their honey bottles, and they may live hanging patiently from the ceiling for years, supplying their anthill with its favorite food, whether honey dew happens to be in season or out.

Honey-cask ants, hanging like storage bottles from the ceiling (left), are fed honey-dew by other members of the anthill.

By reflecting beautiful scenes of the upper world, the surface of the water hides and protects the creatures below.

UNDERWATER
SECRETS

THE SURFACE of water is a thin film that holds together like stretched elastic. It is delicate. It can be punctured and broken easily, but then instantly draws together and mends itself. It can support light objects. You can float a needle on it. Tiny insects called mites run over the surface film. Some are bright red with short legs that do not show. When they run, they look like red balls slipping on ice. An insect called a pond skater runs and leaps on the film without putting its foot through.

The two vast worlds of life on earth, the air world and the water world, are separated by this marvelous thin film. It is transparent, but only when you look nearly straight down through shallow water with a bottom of light sand or light-colored stones. It reflects sky, clouds, trees, and boats of the world above water, and conceals under a magic mirror the creatures and places below.

The inhabitants of the two worlds are so different they might be living on separate planets instead of on opposite sides of a delicate film. Those above take oxygen from fresh air to fill their lungs or breathing tubes; those below breathe with gills—a series of plates which can filter out oxygen dissolved in water.

In the underwater world, fins are used instead of wings, legs for swimming instead of running and jumping. Bodies are shaped like streamlined fish, or they are soft and coiled up in shells as snails, or surrounded with hard armor as are crabs and lobsters.

Even a man changes his appearance when he goes into the underwater world. He can do this only if he takes along air from the world above, so he goes in a submarine that looks like a fish, or wears a diver's helmet and looks like a monster, or he fastens an oxygen tank to his back and goes as a frogman.

But it is not necessary to go underwater to see many strange and beautiful secrets of aquatic life.

On the seashore, between high and low tide, you can see starfish with hundreds of legs, sea urchins like round porcupines, pink sea anemones, purple mussels, snails in spirals of mottled mother-of-pearl. They live in tide pools with little fish and fanciful microscopic life. Flooded at

The surface film of the pond separates two vast worlds.

Crabs, snails, mussels, and starfish live in tidewater pools.

high tide with bubbling salt water, fresh supplies of food arrive at low tide, and sunlight warms the pool with vital supplies of light and energy.

Grunions

Close by these magic pools on the smooth sand where ocean surf crashes and runs, a weird drama is enacted in this world between land and sea, when the mysterious fish called grunions appear. Grunions live in the deep sea. They are seen only once a year, when great numbers slide up the expanses of sandy beach on a full-moon tide—the month's highest tide.

As each wave runs back, grunions flop on the wet sand, helpless as fish out of water. There they lay eggs at the edge of the farthest reach of the sea, burying them in sand, out of sight of hungry shore birds. The eggs are in no danger of washing away because the tides will not be so high again for another month. They receive warmth from the sun and fresh air through the grains of sand.

A month later, at full-moon tide, water creeps up and wets the sand around the eggs. Little grunions break out, ride the waves down, and vanish into the ocean, not to be seen for a year. Then, grown up, they will slide up the beach on a full-moon tide, as their ancestors did.

The Diving Spider

Another remarkable creature is the diving spider, who spends most of his time underwater. His body equipment is no different from that of spiders who live on dry land. Yet this intelligent spider hit on the idea of making a tiny splash at the surface, grabbing a bubble, and hugging it to its chest against its breathing tubes. Then it could stay a long time underwater. When the bubble gets stale, the diving spider swims to the surface, makes another splash, and grabs a fresh bubble.

The diving spider discovers much delicious food in this way. The silent underwater twilight also offers beautiful

The diving spider catches an air bubble at the surface.

He holds it with his hind legs, and adds it to his nest.

places to hide from enemies. So the diving spider builds a home out of splash bubbles and does not come out of the water at all. To fill his home with air, the spider must get both his personal bubble to hug to his chest and an extra one which he carries between his hind legs and puts in the tent. This is the only animal in the world that uses air as a building material. Measuring off the load he can carry with his hind legs, he simply delivers the bubble to his home. After a number of trips, the tent is inflated with enough air to last for weeks.

A male spider building a bubble tent picks a location near the tent of a female spider. He spins a corridor between the two, and fills it with air. He breaks through the partition to the female's tent and air from both tents is joined through the corridor. A terrible fight ensues and both tents are damaged. The male wins, because he is bigger. Then the two repair the tents and settle down to housekeeping and raising a family.

Diving-spider eggs will not hatch under water. They need sunshine, like all spider eggs; so the mother spins a cocoon around them. This bobs to the surface and floats there for a few days until the eggs hatch. Then the babies climb out of the cocoon boat and dive back down to the home tent under the surface.

When the children are old enough to leave home and build their own tents, they take along the first bubble from the family tent as a sort of cornerstone. They may like the smell of family air, or it may inspire them to raise a family.

A dragonfly never folds his wings, even while resting.

The Dragonfly Nymph

The dragonfly is the insect king of the air. Its slender body, three inches long and brightly colored with blue, green, yellow, and red, sparkles in the sunlight. When it lands on a leaf or flower, it does not fold its wings like other insects, but holds them out straight. By whirring it darts, swoops, and stands still in mid-air, and even catches mosquitoes on the wing. It is impossible to imagine the agile dragonfly under water.

But this sprite of the air has another form that lives

underwater, called a dragonfly nymph. It looks like an ugly, fat, dark brown beetle an inch long. It has none of the grace and swiftness of its air-breathing self. It walks clumsily on the dark trash at the bottom of a pond, and it is completely invisible to its prey when it is at rest and perfectly motionless, hiding in the mud.

The dragonfly nymph has no wings, and cannot swim with its legs. It moves through water with a sort of jet propulsion, sucking water into its abdomen and shooting it out like a bellows. It has gills and is able to breathe like a fish, without coming to the surface for air.

The dragonfly nymph has a terrible appetite and eats everything smaller than it is. It hides in the trash, and suddenly its lower lip shoots far out and grabs a victim with pincers. No other animal on earth has a lower lip that turns into lightning pincers like this. When it is not shooting the lip, the pincers are folded under its chin.

When the dragonfly is ready to live in the upper world, its nymph climbs out of the water onto a twig. There in the sunlight its body dries, and its skin splits down the back. The dragonfly steps out of its old skin, wearing four new wings. For an hour it clings to the shell of its former self, drying its wings in the sun. Suddenly it takes off on its first glorious flight into the ocean of air.

It can never go under water again, but when it is time to lay eggs, it flies low over a pond and drops eggs to the bottom. These hatch and new dragonfly nymphs go hunting under water, using their deadly under-lips.

The male stickleback gathers twigs for his nest.

The Stickleback Nest-builder

Of all underwater life, the male stickleback fish leads the busiest existence. Like a bird, he builds a nest of twigs, grass, and whatever he can carry in his mouth. He begins by nosing out a depression in the sand and carrying sand away by the mouthful. When it is built, he digs a tunnel by wriggling under the pile of nest materials. With the nest ready, he waits for a mate.

When a female stickleback turns up, he dances, zigzags, stands on his tail, turns, and swims rapidly toward the nest, while she follows. He points out the tunnel to her.

When she goes in, he prods her to lay eggs. Then he chases her away. Otherwise she will eat the newly laid eggs.

All fish eggs need the touch of air to hatch. So the male faces his eggs, fanning his front fins in reverse. To hold still, he swims forward with his tail. The bubbly current brings fresh air to the eggs and helps them hatch rapidly.

The stickleback has no time to swim lazily around and enjoy himself. The newborn babies are pulled by the attraction of the surface. They pop out of the nest and wriggle toward the light. To save their lives until they can fight for themselves, overworked father stickleback catches them in his mouth and spits them one by one back into the nest. A weird game of tag!

The Anglerfish

The anglerfish is not overworked like the stickleback. It fishes underwater the same way that people sit on the bank and fish with fishing poles in the air world. But the anglerfish performs a magic trick by growing its own fishing pole—right out of the back of its neck!

A long spine grows out of its backbone, over its head and far out in front of its mouth. A bit of flesh shaped like a worm appears at the end of this living fishing pole. Small fish, attracted to the luscious bait, gather around to study it more closely. Then the anglerfish is ready to spring the trap on its victim.

The instant one starts to snap at the bait, the fishing pole

The anglerfish goes fishing with a live fishing pole.

jerks away and the anglerfish does the snapping. It is quicker on the draw.

Another animal using this trick is an alligator turtle in Florida waters. It has a bright spot in the shape of a worm on top of a black tongue. When it opens its mouth, the pink spot looks like a delicious morsel. A fish swims in—and what could be a neater trick for a turtle to get a mouthful?

Fishing with a live fishing pole sounds fantastic, but that is the way with many of the secrets of life under the magic mirror. Even more marvelous is the way the archer fish goes hunting.

The Archer Fish

The archer fish, unlike most other fish, likes to break the surface with its nose and look at the air world. It sees branches of trees and grasses bending low over the water, with moths and caterpillars and other insects sitting on the low-hanging leaves and twigs.

The archer fish can catch such prey, though he can't put more than the tip of his nose out of water. The roof of the archer fish's mouth is grooved so that when the tongue is pressed up against it the groove becomes a pea shooter extending from the back of its mouth straight forward. The gills are a pump, while the tip of the tongue is a valve, swiftly measuring out water bullets one by one.

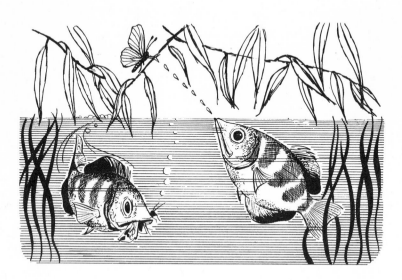

The archer fish shoots water bullets with his eyes underwater.

The pea shooter is invisible. Nothing extends beyond the mouth. It breaks water with its puckery lips and, keeping very still with its eyes under water, it claps its gills, shooting silver bullets rapidly, like a machine gun. The insect is stunned, knocked off the branch into the water, where he struggles and flounders until the archerfish swims close enough to gobble him up.

The archer fish never misses a little insect target within a range of four feet and can score hits up to a distance of as much as twelve feet!

Barnacles

You see them like splashes of whitewash on rocks and wharf piling at low tide. They are hard as rock and so strongly cemented you can't scrape a barnacle off without crushing it. Yet it is born under water as a tiny triangular animal called a nauplius, with one eye, two pairs of legs, and one shell.

In a week or so, the nauplius changes from a little fish that swims freely into an oval animal compressed between two shells like a clam. This animal, called a cypris, has six pairs of legs. When lifted on high tide, it explores for a bare spot where currents are not too strong. Then it puts its head down and presses cement out of its feelers. After that it builds a limestone fortress where it will be a prisoner for the rest of its life.

This weird animal may live five years, half of the time under water and half in the air. The top of the limestone

Colonies of barnacles cling like snow to the rocky shore.

fortress has two plates that revolve to open and close. At low tide, the barnacle is exposed to air, and the trapdoor closes. When the tide comes in, the door opens and out come twelve feathery feet. The barnacle stands on its head and kicks food into its mouth.

Barnacles, unable to swim or walk, can move about by cementing themselves to crabs or jellyfish. They may even find that they travel through all the oceans of the world if they decide to cement themselves onto a whale or onto the hull of a world-traveling freighter.

When a volcano erupts, molten rock spills over the earth.

SECRETS OF STORMS
AND VOLCANOES

NATURE is not always calm. We see the beauty of her serene works, but in the next hour a storm may be raging. Thunder will echo from mountains with a sound that man used to call the rumble of Jove's chariot wheels. Lightning will crack and a tree becomes a blazing fire. In a few hours a living forest and its hidden worlds can be transformed to hot ashes.

Then another secret of life can be seen. Nature is ready to compensate for this calamity. Though fire reduces tall living forests to ashes over and over again through the ages, life returns and rebuilds living places, reseeding the burned-over acres.

Hurricanes are yet another form in which the

elements are hurled at the earth. They madden the sea, sink ships, uproot trees, dash birds from the air, and send floods to sweep away life and destroy living places. It is hard to believe they also create living places for delicate seeds and little ants by tearing down rock and building up new deposits of soil.

In the volcano we again see great forces building an earth to live on. There are about 550 active volcanoes on earth. The Japanese Islands have 54. Many Pacific islands are submarine volcanoes that have grown to the surface.

The volcano Fujiyama is a Japanese shrine. Sweeping up from sea level more than 12,000 feet, it is like a glorious holy pyramid. Day and night, a column of pilgrims trickles up and down the steep slopes of lava ash, to see a crater whose depths exhale wisps of steam, whispering of a power beyond the imagination of man.

The greatest active volcano in the world today is Mauna Loa in Hawaii. It pours out enormous masses of land in the form of lava; they will be the living places of future animals. Mauna Loa is nearly 15,000 feet above the Pacific, but its slopes plunge down another 15,000 feet under water. Its real height exceeds that of Mt. Everest, the highest mountain on earth. Mauna Loa has coughed up so much lava that its base now occupies 3,900 square miles—built up by molten rock trickling down its sides—giving it the largest base of any mountain in the world.

In the United States we have scenic volcanoes in the Cascade system of the Northwest: Rainier, Adams, Hood,

Lassen Peak has erupted in recent years.

Mauna Loa in Hawaii spills tons of lava from its crater.

Shasta. They are silent, without any wisps of steam. Snow-topped Lassen Peak is seen by air passengers out of San Francisco. Lassen stood cold and still in the history of man until 1914. Then a hot puff—filled with dust and rocks—flattened neighboring trees, and doughy red lava flowed out of its crater and down its sides. Today Lassen sleeps again, blanketed in snow.

In 1943, below our Mexican border, a farmer walking barefooted through his corn patch felt the ground was hot. Scared, he ran to the village priest. A few days later he saw smoke coming up from the plowed furrows of his field.

This time the villagers all came to see; they stared and babbled, terrified to see the cracks in the earth and the rising column of ashes and smoke.

Soon a cone formed—Paricutín, the world's newest volcano. Springs went dry. Birds dropped dead out of the sky. Trees withered and turned black. In four months, Paricutín rose over a thousand feet. It has given scientists their only chance to photograph, study, take temperatures, and write about a volcano from the beginning. Some day it may top Popocatepetl's 17,880 feet; more likely it will go to sleep as a handsome adolescent volcano. Man can't even begin to guess.

Steam rises as the fiery streams of lava reach the sea.

A black crust forms on top of the cooling lava.

Today's volcanoes are creating living places for a future life that is beyond imagination. The living soil is built of lava and rock, sediment and dust. It forms slowly. In a hundred years an inch of fertile soil will form. Quietly, in the darkness, soil mixes the brew of life supplied by the elements. It is made ready expressly for little white root hairs that will suck it up to produce food for all the animals and plants on the face of the earth. Then it remains only for a seed to find a place in the soil, where it can send down its root, unfurl its first green leaves, and set the cycle of life in motion once again.

An asterisk (°) denotes pages that are illustrated.

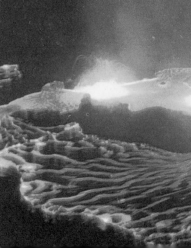